LOGIC GAMES

COMPILED BY
NORMAN BARRETT

Kingfisher Books

Kingfisher Books, Grisewood & Dempsey Ltd
Elsley House, 24-30 Great Titchfield Street, London W1P 7AD

First published in 1992 by Kingfisher Books
10 9 8 7 6 5 4

British Library Cataloguing in Publication Data
A catalogue record of this book is available from the British Library.

ISBN 0 86272 904 1

Editor : John Grisewood
Design : Mustafa Sidki
Cover Design : Terry Woodley

Printed and bound in Hong Kong

Cover Illustration : Can you get out of a maze? There
is one sure – but long – way out of any maze. Keeping
one wall always to one side of you, follow it and
eventually you'll escape!

CONTENTS

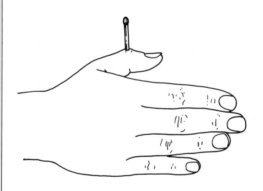

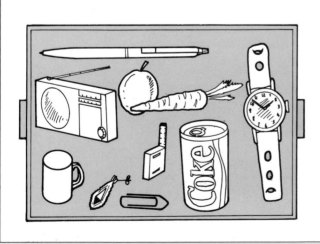

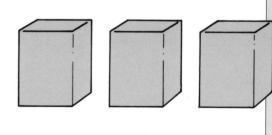

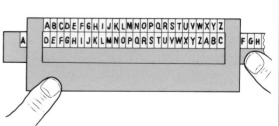

1 LATERAL THINKING

Most problems in logic may be worked out step-by-step, each step leading logically to the next one. This is sometimes called "vertical thinking". But some problems cannot be solved in this way. You might have to find an unusual method or an unexpected answer. We call this "lateral thinking". Many problems and puzzles call for both types of thinking - lateral thinking to put you on the right track and then vertical, step-by-step thinking to get to the correct solution.

Father and son

Two Americans met to have lunch. One was the father of the other one's son. How were they related to each other?

Bottles and knives

Dr Edward de Bono, who invented the term "lateral thinking", devised this problem. You have three bottles forming a triangle. Using three knives that are not long enough to reach from one bottle to another, can you form a platform across the bottles which will support a glass of water?

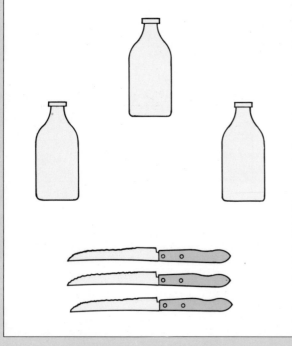

The dream

A doctor and a detective were having a discussion about their cases. The doctor told the detective the story of a man who was watching a film on television with his wife. It was a "gangster" film involving car chases and shooting. The man, however, fell asleep, and in his dream he found himself taking part in the story he had been watching on television. He was driving his car and being chased by some villains. He came to a railway crossing, and decided to take a risk and crash through the barrier. As he crossed the line, he caught sight of an express train roaring down upon him. Meanwhile, on the television, the film ended, and the man's wife switched off the set and, noticing that her husband was asleep, shook him by the shoulder. It was just at that moment in his dream that the express train was about to hit him. The shock was so great that the man collapsed and died instantly.

"I don't believe that," said the detective, "it's absolute nonsense." What made him come to that conclusion?

Houses and pipes

The plan shows three houses marked A, B and C. All are in an enclosed private square. At the entrance to the square are the mains supplies for gas (G), electricity (E) and water (W). Each of the houses needs only one of these services - house A only water, house B only gas, and house C only electricity. The pipes from the mains must be laid in such a way that they reach the houses requiring them without crossing each other or going outside the square. How can this be done?

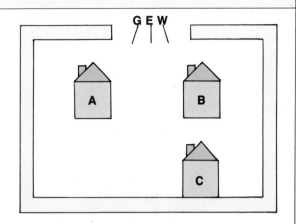

Cutting a postcard

Here's a puzzle that might seem impossible at first. Take an ordinary postcard. Now cut it, keeping it in one piece, so that an ordinary person can step through it!

Multiplying amoebas

There are two similar jars containing the same amount of water. In one of the jars is one amoeba and in the second jar are two amoebas, It is well known that amoebas reproduce themselves when they have grown large enough by splitting into two.

   The amoebas in these jars take five minutes to reproduce themselves. If it takes the amoebas in the second jar fours hours to fill the jar with amoebas, how long does it take the one amoeba in the first jar to do the same?

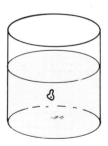 

The portrait

A visitor to a house sees a portrait and asks who it is. The owner replies in rhyme:

   "Uncles and brothers have I none,
   But that man's father is my father's son."

Who is portrayed in the picture?

The next letter

What is the next letter in this series:

O T T F F S S

Unspillable water

This is a good trick, but make sure you do it in the kitchen. What you have to do is this. Fill a glass with water and place it in such a position that it cannot be lifted without spilling all of the water.

   See if you can think of a way of doing this before looking at the answer.

5

Only one match

You reach the holiday home just as it begins to get dark. There is no one else around. When you open the door, you find there is no electricity. You have only one match, and there is a log fire, a paraffin lamp and a gas fire. What should you light first?

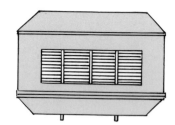

Foxy Foxwell

The head of a big engineering factory was very concerned about the loss of tools, equipment and other things through stealing by the workers. He decided to appoint a security officer who would be responsible for detecting any more thefts. The new security person, a Mr Hawkins, was duly taken on. "Most of my employees are honest," said the governor, "but it isn't fair if a few dishonest people are getting away with it." "Don't worry," said Hawkins, "I'll give the matter all my attention."

After a few weeks, matters started to improve, but Hawkins was not satisfied. Things were still disappearing, and he was suspicious, in particular, of a certain person called Joe Foxwell. Joe, known by his friends as "Foxy", regularly took a wheelbarrow full of all kinds of junk out of the factory and down to the local dump. Each time he left the factory, Hawkins made a thorough search of Foxy's barrow and person. But he found nothing but rusty bits of metal, broken parts and other useless rubbish.

This went on for years, until Foxy eventually retired and left the factory for good. Many years later, Hawkins, who had moved on to another job, met Foxy in a pub. The two of them naturally began to chat about the old times in the engineering factory.

"You know, Foxy, I always suspected you, and I still think you were pinching something."

"I'll tell you the truth," said Foxy, "I was."

"I knew it," cried Hawkins. "But what was it you were taking?"

Can you guess what Foxy was stealing?

A handy trick

Ask someone to hold their hands out in front of them. Tell them that you can put something in their left hand which they cannot possibly take out with their right.
    What is it?

There's no law against it!

A well-known lawyer was answering listeners' questions on a radio phone-in programme. One man rang up and said he wanted some information concerning the marriage laws. He would like to know if the law allows a man to marry his widow's sister.
    "The law has nothing to say on the matter," answered the lawyer. "But if you are the man in question, I very much doubt if you'll ever get the opportunity!"
    Why should this be so?

Hard-boiled eggs

It is a well-known fact that eating too many hard-boiled eggs can make you constipated. Can you say how many hard-boiled eggs it is safe for a hungry person to eat on an empty stomach?

Family fun

A man and his wife have seven sons, and every one of the sons has a sister. How many are there altogether in the family.

2 MATCH MANIPULATION

You can use matches for all kinds of puzzles, tricks and games. It is a good idea to collect a box or two of used matches, as they are safe to play with. Never play with live matches unless there is an adult present.

Halving the squares

Set out 15 matches in the pattern shown below. There are six squares (don't forget the larger one!). Now remove three of the matches, without moving any of the others, and turn the six squares into three.

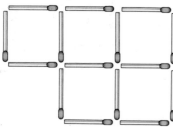

Squarebashing

To make up the pattern below you will need 24 matches.

(a) Take away eight matches, without moving any of the others, to leave six squares.

(b) Starting with the same arrangement of 24 matches, again take away just eight matches, this time to leave only two squares.

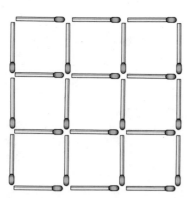

More squares

Set 12 matches out in the arrangement shown below. Now move just two matches to make seven squares.

Pigpens

Farmer Albert Crookfoot had six pigs which he wanted to keep separate because they were always fighting. He made the pens as shown in the diagram, using 13 large pieces of wood the same size. One of the bits of wood was badly damaged in a storm, however, so he had to rebuild the pens with only 12.

Using 12 matches, can you work out how he redesigned the pigpens?

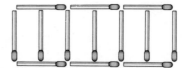

Nim games

The various versions of Nim are games for two people played with a set number of matches or any number of matches. (You can also play Nim with coins, paper-clips or even small bits of paper.)

In Nim games, the players take turns to remove matches. The winner is the player who forces his or her opponent to take the last match.

Nim in rows

Set out 15 matches in three rows, as shown:

The rules are as follows:
   (1) The two players take turns to remove a match or matches.
   (2) Players may remove any number of matches on their turn, provided they take from only one row.
   (3) Players must remove at least one match on each turn.
   (4) The winner is the player who forces his opponent to take the last match.

Nim has been played for hundreds or even thousands of years. It might have begun in ancient China. Mathematicians have studied it, argued about it and written learned papers about it. It was an American mathematician, Charles Bouton, who in 1901 first called the game Nim, probably from an English word no longer in use meaning to "take".

Nim tactics

The more you play Nim, the better you become. You will begin to recognize the patterns, or combinations, to aim for in order to win. For example, if you leave your opponent with one match in each row, that is 1 − 1 − 1, you must win. (That's easy enough to work out for yourself.) Another winning combination is 2 − 2 − 0. Whether your opponent takes one or two from a row, it is simple then to leave just one and win. Try working out for yourself why 3 − 2 − 1 is another winning combination to leave your opponent.

One, two, three Nim

In this version of Nim, you can play with any number of matches, although some people play with a set number such as 15 or 21. The matches may be set out in a single row or scattered about in no particular pattern.

The important rule in this version of Nim is that each player must remove either one, two or three matches at each turn. Again, the one who takes the last match is the loser.

The tactics here involve leaving your opponent with a certain number of matches. If, for example, you leave five matches, you must win. However many your opponent takes, you can leave just one on your next go. The secret is to leave one plus any multiple of four. Say you leave 13 matches (4 + 4 + 4 + 1). However many your opponent removes, you make it up to four. If they take one, you take three. If they take two, you take two. And if they take three, you take one.

Sooner or later your opponent will cotton on to these winning tactics. If you both know the secret, the only way to play is to move fast. Then, the winner will be the one who is quickest to spot a winning combination.

Reverse Nim

If you get tired of playing your favourite version of Nim, you can always reverse the rules. In this case, the one who takes the last match is the winner. Reverse Nim involves a new set of winning combinations. You can work these out for yourself!

Making nines

This one sounds impossible, but it can be done. Take eleven matches. Without removing any, see if you can sort them out so that they make nine.

Now take just three matches and turn them into nine!

Touching matches

Here's a tricky puzzle. Take six matches. Now set them out so that each match touches all the other matches.

A Roman problem

What's wrong with this simple equation, made up with 11 matches and using Roman numerals?

The answer is that three minus two equals one, not four. By moving just one match, you can make an equation that is correct. In fact, there are two separate ways of doing this. Can you find them?

Triangulation

Take six matches. Can you make four equal triangles with them? Here's a clue - you might need glue!

Making triangles

Set nine matches out to make the three triangles as shown below.

  (a) Move two matches to make four triangles.

  (b) Start again with the same three triangles. Now move three matches to make five triangles. It can be done!

Match trick

Take a match from a book of matches, not a box. Throw it in the air and see if it lands on its edge. No? Try again. No matter how many times you try, it will always land flat on its side.

  Now you must put your thinking cap on. It can be done!

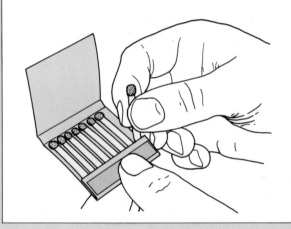

The first matches
An English chemist, John Walker, invented the match in 1827. His matches, which became known as "lucifers", were made of wooden splints about 8 centimetres long, tipped with a mixture of chemicals. To light one, a person had to draw it through a material like sandpaper. Lucifers often showered their users with sparks.

The little square

Here's a good trick you can catch your friends with. Set out four matches in a cross like this:

Make sure you place the matches with heads away from the centre and with the central gap closed, but do it quickly without giving the game away.

Now ask your friends to make a square with the four matches by moving only one match.

They will think of all sorts of silly things, but when they give up, all you have to do is pull one match a couple of millimetres outwards. This makes a tiny square in the middle of the four matches.

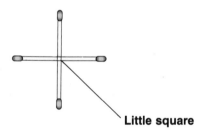

Little square

A balancing trick

Have you ever tried balancing a stick on the back of your thumb? It isn't too difficult after a little practice. You can try it with an umbrella or a tennis racket. But you probably won't be able to do it with a pencil, and you certainly can't do it with a match. Or can you?

This is a trick you can catch your friends with. First ask them if they can stand a match on their thumb as shown here:

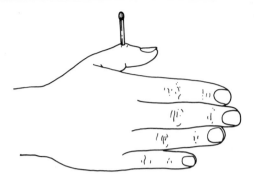

As hard as they try, they won't succeed. When they have finished trying, you can casually take a match and show them how it's done.

The secret is to prepare a match beforehand. You make a small split at the foot of the match, not big enough to be noticeable. (Ask an adult to do this for you with a knife.) You then place the match on the joint of your slightly bent thumb, and straighten the thumb as you do it. A small fold of skin will catch in the split of the match and hold it upright. You will need a little practice to get this right.

The match challenge

This is a good party trick. Ask someone to provide a box of matches. Then challenge your friends to say, without opening the box, at which end the heads of the matches are. They have to be absolutely certain. Otherwise they must pay a nasty forfeit!

They will try all sorts of things, such as shaking the box and listening. But this won't help. When they give up, you take the box, put the centre of it across a finger and balance it. The end with the heads is heavier, and will tip down.

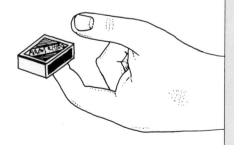

3 ODD ONE OUT

In each of the groups on these pages there is one item that, in some way, does not belong. For example, if there was a group FOOTBALL, BASEBALL, BOXING and CRICKET, the odd one out would be BOXING, because the other three are all team sports.

See if you can say which is the odd one out in the groups here, and also say why.

1 Dolphin
Shark
Seal
Walrus

2 Egypt
Ghana
Zimbabwe
Pretoria

3 Shakespeare
Michelangelo
Leonardo Da Vinci
Salvador Dali

4 Bat
Robin
Owl
Vulture

5 Steam
Smoke
Ice
Water

6 Violin
Lyre
Xylophone
Harp

7 Circle
Square
Cube
Hexagon

8 New York City
Toronto
Los Angeles
Detroit

10 Yen
Cent
Metre
Rand

11 Alps
Andes
Everglades
Appalachians

12 Eggs
Milk
Butter
Cheese

13 Tennis
Squash
Badminton
Table-Tennis

14 Methane
Plutonium
Carbon dioxide
Nitrogen

15 Nile
Mississippi
Ganges
Superior

16 Backgammon
Canasta
Rummy
Bridge

17 Mercury
Uranus
Sirius
Neptune

9

Lion

Tiger

Tabby

Greyhound

18

Ostrich

Kiwi

Eagle

Penguin

19

Queen of Hearts

Queen of Spades

Jack of Spades

King of Hearts

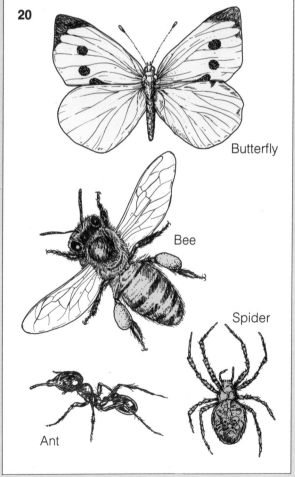

20

Butterfly

Bee

Spider

Ant

13

4 FUN WITH COINS

Coins are ideal for many tricks and puzzles. Most are perfectly round, they have two different sides, and people carry them around in their pockets. They also have different values. Coins have been used for money for thousands of years, and some of the oldest problems concern coins.

A "coin-fidence" trick

The coin pictured here (both sides shown) was taken by a farmer to a London auction house. He claimed to have found it while digging up a field. He said that he knew his farm covered an ancient Roman encampment, because he had found one or two relics in the past. But this was a fine coin, and in remarkable condition. He would like it put into the firm's next sale.

An expert on ancient coins examined the coin, and immediately turned to the farmer and said: "I'm afraid we can't accept this. In fact you can count yourself lucky that we are not reporting you to the police."

What made the expert so angry?

The disappearing coin

Here's a trick you can play at a party. You'll need a piece of double-sided sticky tape attached to your thumb.

Show a small coin, such as a penny, and ask someone to hold their hand out. Now tell them to shut their eyes, and then place the coin in their open hand. Press down firmly on the coin with your thumb (the one with the sticky tape) so they can really feel the coin. Then take away your hand, at the same time closing theirs with your other hand.

"Have you got it?", you ask them. "Yes", they say. You intone the magic words, "Abracadabra, coin, coin go away," and then ask them to open their eyes and hand. Of course they haven't got the coin. It's disappeared - into your pocket if you've been clever enough to slip it off your thumb unnoticed.

The cup catch

Another party trick. Turn a cup upside-down on a table and put a thin coin on it. Tell your friends they can have the coin if they can lift it off the top of the cup without touching the cup.

This doesn't seem too difficult, so you won't be short of volunteers. Someone will have a go and will lift the coin very carefully between their fingernails and triumphantly claim it.

"Sorry," you will say, "I said to lift it off the top of the cup, and you lifted it off the bottom!"

Touching coins

Set out six same-sized coins in two rows as shown here:

The problem is to change the two rows into a circle by moving three of the coins, one at a time, without disturbing any of the others. You may slide the coins, but not lift them.

Space for No. 5

Here is a problem that is more difficult than it looks. Set out four same-sized coins in the way shown below so that there is space for a fifth coin to be inserted to touch the other four.

No other coins may be used before you introduce the fifth coin, and no means of measurement may be used other than the four coins themselves (that's a good hint). You may only slide coins, not lift them.

Don't try to set the coins out by your eye alone. That's guesswork, and you'd probably get it wrong anyway. The coins should finish up as above.

Changing places

Set out six coins in the manner shown below, starting with three heads, followed by a space, and then three tails. Number the coins and space from one to seven.

The problem is to make the heads and tails change places, so that you finish with heads in spaces 5-7 and tails in 1-3. You must follow certain rules in the way you move the coins. (1) You may move any coin one space along into an empty space. (2) You may jump a coin over a coin next to it into an empty space (as in draughts). (3) Most importantly, you may move heads only to the right and tails only to the left.

The problem can be solved in 15 moves.

Up-ending the pyramid

Set out ten coins in a pyramid as shown here:

Now, by moving just three coins, turn the pyramid upside-down.

A simple sum

You have two coins in your pocket which make up 25 pence. But one of the coins is not a 20p piece. What are the two coins?

5 A WAY WITH WORDS

Words can be fascinating, even when you don't know their meaning. Take "syzygy" for example. That's a fine word - six letters, three syllables and no vowels! Well, that's not quite true, because the letter "y" used as here is really a vowel.

By the way, it is a term used in astronomy and means the period of a new or a full moon.

Many kinds of puzzles are based on words - their spelling, their meaning or their pronunciation.

Word records

Vowels

There are five vowels in the English alphabet - A E I O U - six if you count Y.

The shortest word to contain all five vowels in alphabetical order is FACETIOUS. In fact, we can go one better and make the shortest word to contain all six vowels: FACETIOUSLY.

Can you think of a five-letter word that has four vowels? And what about a word that has five vowels in a row? Or an eight-letter word that has only one vowel?

Consonants

There are 21 consonants in the English alphabet. A word that has six consonants in a row is laTCHSTRing (a cord enabling a door latch to be raised from the outside). Can you think of a word that has five consonants in a row? It has to do with magic.

Letter pairs

Here's a difficult one. Can you think of a word that has three pairs of letters in a row? To give you a clue, the answer is a word made up from two easy words and means "someone who writes out accounts".

Before and after

Can you make a six-letter word meaning a "public speaker" by adding the same two letters before and after AT ? Now try an eleven-letter word by putting the same three letters before and after ERGRO? A clue - it's a type of railway.

Sounds the same

Words that have the same sound but different meanings are called "homonyms". An example of a pair of homonyms is HART and HEART. Sometimes there are more than two, such as RIGHT, RITE, WRIGHT and WRITE. These are all pronounced alike but have different meanings.

With the help of the clues, see how many of the following pairs of homonyms you can find:

1 (a) conifer tree, (b) soft hair
2 (a) an army officer, (b) inside of a nut
3 (a) one who sells, (b) underground room
4 (a) seep out, (b) onion-like vegetable
5 (a) cat-like animal, (b) joining pieces
6 (a) a bird's "collar", (b) not smooth
7 (a) fibber, (b) stringed instrument
8 (a) church corridor, (b) island
9 (a) golf starting place, (b) a drink
10 (a) daring, (b) rolled a ball
11 (a) small fruit, (b) put in ground
12 (a) convent woman, (b) not one
13 (a) junior, (b) underground worker
14 (a) kind of ape, (b) rebel fighter
15 (a) weight, (b) barrel
16 (a) stitch, (b) plant seeds
17 (a) coin, (b) smell
18 (a) seashore, (b) tree
19 (a) step, (b) gaze
20 (a) frog-like animal, (b) pulled along

Double words

Homonyms that have the same spelling but different meanings are called double words. For example, BEAR is an animal but also means "to support or carry", and TILL is a money-drawer and also means "to cultivate".

Below are 20 pairs of clues, or definitions, to double words. See how many you can solve.

1 to stop up - a wooden shoe
2 tomb - serious
3 artist - rope on a boat
4 invoice - beak
5 summit - spinning toy
6 bread - loiter
7 lord - pry or peep
8 apartment - level
9 jump - ingredient of beer
10 a dessert - a small amount
11 a business - not easily moved
12 printing - kind or sort
13 circle - peal
14 fruit - day and month
15 hut - to cast off
16 bend over - thin
17 to train - part of a train
18 stingy - average
19 pot - ship
20 cudgel - society

Back-and-forth words

Words that spell the same way backwards are called "palindromes". Examples are BOB, ROTOR and MADAM. The longest word palindrome in English is REDIVIDER, which has nine letters.

See if you can think of palindromes which have the following meanings:

1 A sheep (3 letters)
2 An action (4)
3 To take a look (4)
4 Midday (4)

5 Flat (5)
6 Canoe (5)
7 A musical note (5)
8 Made into a god (7)

Anagrams

An anagram is a word or phrase formed from the letters of another word or phrase in a different order. For example, POST and STOP are anagrams of each other.

Can you find anagrams of the following with the help of the clues in brackets?

1 SORE (flower)
2 THAN SLEEP (animals)
3 AND SHOUT (a number)
4 BET NAILS TEN (a sport)
5 NIGHT AS NOW (American state)
6 BUS IN MARE (ship)
7 STORM LEARNING (astronaut)
8 WE ALL MAKE HIS PRAISE (playwright)
9 A MAN EVADED (first pair)
10 AN ASK LETTER (reptile)

It is fun to find anagrams that are related to each other in some way. For example, ENRAGED and ANGERED mean the same thing, and HERE COME DOTS is a clue to THE MORSE CODE.

Try these:

11 MOON-STARERS (one word)
12 NINE THUMPS (one word)
13 THEY SEE (two words)
14 THE CLASSROOM (one word)
15 ONE IS APART (one word)
16 ONE PLUS TWELVE (three words)

Finally, see if you can you make one word from NEW DOOR, but don't spend too long on it!

Spot the error

"There is three mistakes in this sentence."
Can you find them?

Doublets

Lewis Carroll, who wrote *Alice in Wonderland*, invented the doublet. This is a puzzle or game where you change one word into another, letter by letter, and each step must be a proper word. The aim is to complete the doublet in as few steps as possible. The game has other names, such as "ladderwords" and "stepwords".

It is fun to choose two words that are either similar or opposite. Just make sure that they have the same number of letters, and that they do not contain the same letter in the same place.

For example, you can go from LESS to MORE in four steps, which is the best possible for four-letter words:

LESS
LOSS
LOSE
LORE
MORE

Try the following, and see how many steps you need:

1 CAT into DOG
2 POOR into RICH
3 LIVE into DEAD
4 DUST into GOLD
5 BLACK into WHITE

Now make up your own doublets. You can play doublets as a game. Choose a pair of words and see who can complete the change in the fewest steps.

The word-square game

This game may be played by several players, but is best suited to two, three or four. All you need are pencils and paper. Draw a five-by-five square as shown here, making 25 squares in all. The players should not be able to see each other's squares.

Each player calls out a letter in turn, and every player has to write down that letter in one of the 25 squares. Players choose for themselves where they put the letters, but once written in a letter may not be moved or changed.

The game continues until all the squares are filled. For the very last letter, the 25th, the players may choose any letter they like.

The idea is to make words, reading either down or across from left to right. At the end of the game, these words earn points - 10 for a 5-letter word, 5 for a 4-letter word, and 3 for a 3-letter word. Two-letter words and proper nouns do not score. An example of a completed square and the points awarded is shown here.

P	A	N	I	C
R	I	O	T	O
A	L	O	E	S
T	E	N	M	T
E	D	I	T	S

PANIC	10	PRATE	10
RIOT	5	AILED	10
ALOES	10	NOON	5
TEN	3	ITEM	5
EDITS	10	COSTS	10
		Total	78

NOTE: Only one score may be earned on each line. For example, you cannot claim PAN as well as PANIC, or AIL as well as AILED.

Word squares

If you managed to fill a 25-letter square with five 5-letter words going across and the same five going down, you would have made up a "word square". Here is an example:

CRUST
RANCH
UNDER
SCENE
THREE

It is quite difficult to make up word squares with 5-letter words. Have a try at making up smaller word squares. Here are some examples:

MAN
APE
NEW

FEN
EWE
NET

NICE
IRON
CORD
ENDS

Word-finding

In each of the three squares shown here some words have been hidden. What you have to do, moving from square to square, is trace out a series of words or names. You can start at any letter you like, but to help you on your way, the best letter to start with in Square No. 1 is one of the B's. You can go from one letter to the next by moving across one little square at a time, left, right, up, down or diagonally. You may not use any of the letters more than once, and all 25 letters must be used. Clues to each puzzle are given underneath.

1 Five colours

W	N	E	N	Y
O	G	R	E	E
R	W	O	L	L
B	B	E	E	V
L	U	M	A	U

2 Four countries

Y	N	A	M	R
E	M	N	I	E
X	I	D	O	G
A	I	C	L	D
I	C	E	A	N

3 Five animals

B	R	H	C	A
E	A	E	E	P
Z	L	E	A	H
S	E	T	I	L
A	E	W	N	O

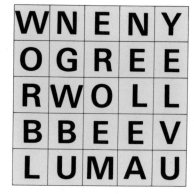

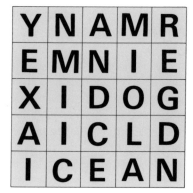

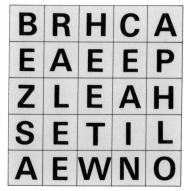

6 PARADOXES

A paradox is something that appears absurd but may turn out to be true. There are some problems that seem to defy logic. At first glance, they might appear to be impossible to work out. In some cases, there seems to be an obvious answer which then turns out to be wrong. This is usually because you miss the main point or you pay too much attention to the wrong thing. It pays to treat the question with suspicion!

Bottle and cork

Here's a simple one to start with. A bottle and a cork together cost a drinks manufacturer 11 pence. The bottle costs 10p more than the cork. How much does the cork cost?

Packing them in

On a package holiday to Spain, six couples turned up late on Saturday night and found their hotel overbooked. There were only five rooms available.

But the manager had a brain-wave. He took the first couple to the first room and asked another couple to stay with them while he sorted things out. Then he took the third couple to the second room, the fourth couple to the third room, and the fifth couple to the fourth room. He then returned to the first room for the sixth couple and put them in the fifth room.

So every couple had their own room and were quite happy. Or were they?

A basket of eggs

A farmer's wife took a basket of free-range eggs to market. She sold half her eggs plus half an egg to her first customer. Then she sold half the eggs left plus half an egg to her next customer, half what was left plus half an egg to her third customer, and finally half the eggs left plus half an egg to her fourth customer. This left her with one egg, which she took home for the farmer's lunch.

How many eggs did she start with? Oh, by the way, she didn't break any eggs. (Note: It's important that they were all free-range eggs.)

Dividing up the gold

A train was chugging across the desert on a hot, dry day. Most of the passengers had brought water with them for the long journey, but a little old man was sitting in the corner with nothing to drink. Two passengers, friends from a poor village, offered to share their water with the old man. One had five bottles and the other three, and they shared the water equally among the three of them.

On leaving the train, the old man, who turned out to be a rich businessman, took eight gold coins from his purse and gave them to the two friends in thanks for their kindness. He suggested they share them in proportion to their contribution of water.

But when the two friends got back to their village, they could not agree how many coins they each should get. What was the right solution?

20

The missing pound

Three people were dining together at a restaurant. Their bill came to £30 and each of them gave the waiter a £10 note. When he took the money to the cash desk, the cashier explained that there had been a mistake in totalling the bill. It should have been £25, so the cashier gave the waiter five £1 coins to return to the diners.

But, as the waiter returned to the dining room, he began to have dishonest thoughts. Why should he return all the money? The diners would be none the wiser, and anyway they would only find it difficult to split £5 among the three of them. So he returned £3 and kept the remaining £2.

The problem is this. The diners each received £1 back, so their meals cost them £9 each, making £27. The waiter had kept £2. That's £29 altogether. Yet they originally handed over £30. What happened to the other pound?

Passing trains

An express train leaves Omsk for Plomsk at the same time as a stopping train leaves Plomsk for Omsk. The express travels at a steady 130 km/h, while the slower train averages 80 km/h. Which train is farther from Omsk when they meet?

Sharing the elephants

An Indian raja died and left his 17 elephants to his three sons. In his will, he left half the elephants to his eldest son, a third to his middle son, and a ninth to his youngest son.

This puzzled the three sons. Half of 17 is 8½. Three won't go into 17 either. How were they going to divide the elephants among themselves in accordance with their father's wishes without cutting up some of the animals?

Then the youngest son had an idea. Let's ask the temple priest. He's a wise old man. So they called the priest and told him about their problem. He thought for a few moments, got up and said he would be back shortly. When he returned a few minutes later, he was leading the temple elephant. "Here," he said, "I'm going to lend you this elephant and we'll solve your problem."

He put the temple elephant in with the brothers' 17 elephants, making 18 altogether. He told the eldest brother to take half the elephants, which was nine, the middle brother a third, which was six, and the youngest a ninth, which was two. That just left the temple elephant, which he proceeded to take back to the temple.

So the instructions of the raja were followed precisely. Or were they?

7 CODES AND SECRETS

Writing secret messages is fun. Some codes are simple and can be "cracked" easily. For example, in the message TEEM EM TA EHT LOOHCS ETAG, the words have been spelled backwards.

Knowing the secret of the code, it's very easy to read the message. But even if you didn't know the "key", as it's called, you would probably be able to work it out fairly quickly for yourself.

Simple ciphers

When messages are coded by using letters to stand for other letters, it is called a "cipher". More than 2,000 years ago, the Roman general Julius Caesar used a simple cipher to send secret messages home from his campaigns abroad. For each letter he substituted the letter three places to the right in the alphabet. For example, A became D, B became E and so on.

You can do this yourself by writing the alphabet out on one line and then, below it, another alphabet starting with D and ending with C:

A B C D E F G H I J K L M N O P Q R S T U V W X Y Z
D E F G H I J K L M N O P Q R S T U V W X Y Z A B C

Using Caesar's cipher, see if you can decipher the following message:

WKH HQHPB VROGLHUV DUH WZR GDBV PDUFK DZDB

Changing the code

Using the same letter to represent another letter, as in Caesar's cipher, will not fool people for very long. The next step is to change the code. You can use the fourth letter to the right in the alphabet, or the ninth, the 15th and so on.

Instead of writing out alphabets every time you want to use a new code, it is a good plan to make a simple cipher slide. Write out a full alphabet on one strip of paper and two full alphabets on another. It is important that each letter takes up exactly the same space, so use squared paper or type your letters. By sliding one strip above the other, you can change your codes.

Now see if you can encipher (put into code) the following message by using a code based on the fourth letter to the right - that is, place A above E:

REINFORCEMENTS NEEDED

Next, decipher the following message by using a code based on the seventh letter to the right - that is, place A above H:

LMKBDX TM WTPG

Making a cipher slide

If you want to change codes after every word or even every letter, you will need a proper cipher slide. This is not difficult to make. To do this, you stick your single alphabet on a piece of card. Then cut two slots beneath the alphabet as shown in the diagram.

Now stick your double alphabet on a thin strip of card to slide through the slots.

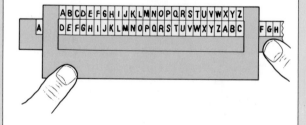

Using a codeword

If you want to make it really difficult, or almost impossible, for someone to break your code, you can change your cipher after every letter. To do this, and for a friend to be able to decipher your message, you need a codeword.

Say, for example, you choose QUICK as your codeword. Then for the first letter of your message you will use the Q cipher, placing Q under A on your slide cipher. For the second letter, you use the U cipher, and so on. After using the K cipher for the fifth letter, you start with Q again for your sixth letter.

Try using this codeword to encipher the instruction ATTACK. Great care is called for to do this correctly. But as soon as you get the hang of it you will be able to encipher longer messages quite quickly.

Deciphering such messages also calls for care and patience. Using the same codeword, QUICK, see how quickly you can decipher the following message: FOUREBE.

(right column top)

This type of code was used by soldiers in the American Civil War and was known as the Pigpen cipher, from the shape of the grid. Now you can work out the message above.

The letters in the above system have been entered in the grids in a regular order. If you want to make the code more difficult to break, you can make up you own order. A good plan is to use a "key word". Choose a word or name that does not have any repeated letters, such as FRIEND or DOUGLAS, and write these in across the top of the grid. Follow this with the remaining letters of the alphabet, filling in the grid in rows across. Let's use CHRISTABEL for our key word - it has 10 letters, all different. The grid will now look like this:

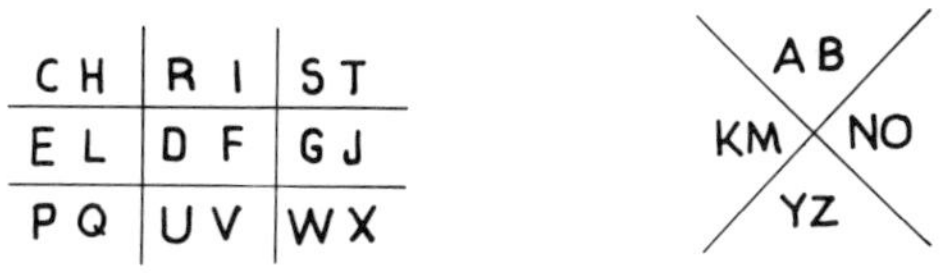

C H	R I	S T
E L	D F	G J
P Q	U V	W X

Try making up your own messages using this Pigpen cipher.

Secret symbols

Before you read on, see if you can guess what sort of code this is:

The symbols look like a strange language, ancient Egyptian perhaps, but they are diagram ciphers. They are formed by grouping the letters in pairs and placing them in simple grids, as here:

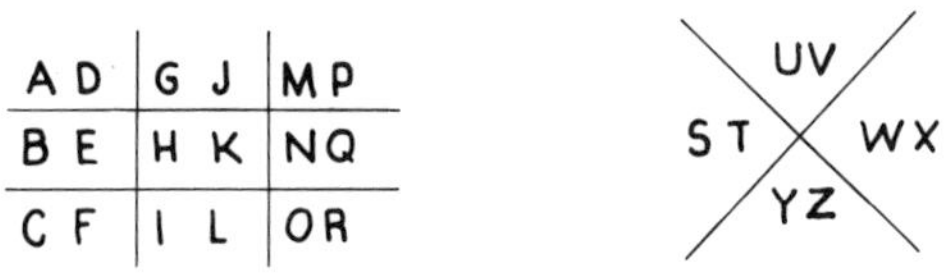

A D	G J	M P
B E	H K	N Q
C F	I L	O R

You encipher a message by using the part of the grid in which a letter stands, adding a dot if the letter is the second one of the pair. For example,

A = ⌐   D = •⌐   K = ⊡   Z = ⩘

Tramps' code

Tramps, who travel around the country looking for the odd job or some food, perhaps, have a code of their own. This is a picture code which they chalk up outside houses to help other tramps.

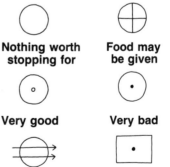

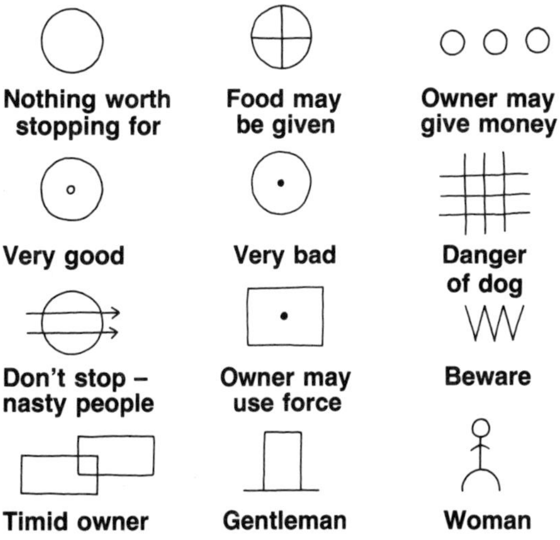

Nothing worth stopping for   Food may be given   Owner may give money

Very good   Very bad   Danger of dog

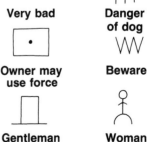

Don't stop – nasty people   Owner may use force   Beware

Timid owner   Gentleman   Woman

Spoken codes

Spoken codes are great fun - unless you have to listen to people speaking to each other in code and you don't understand it!

A popular spoken code is called Pig Latin, although it has nothing to do with Latin (or even pigs). It's just a simple way of mixing up words to confuse anyone you don't want to listen to your conversation.

To speak Pig Latin, all you need to know are the two rules. (1) For words beginning with a vowel, just add -WAY at the end. For example, AM becomes AMWAY, ANNE becomes ANNEWAY. (2) For words beginning with a consonant, take the consonant (or consonant sound if it is more then one letter) to the end of the word and then add -AY. So MAN becomes ANMAY, PETER becomes ETERPAY, and SCHOOL becomes OOLSCHAY.

This might look very simple when written down, but when spoken quickly Pig Latin sounds like a foreign language. It calls for plenty of practice.

See how quickly you can work out what the following means:

ODAY OUYAY IKELAY IMHAY ? IWAY ODAY

There are plenty of other spoken codes. In Opish, you add -OP after each consonant. For example, PIN becomes POPINOP, CART becomes COPAROPTOP. In Turkey Irish, you add AB- before each vowel, so PIN is PABIN, ENEMY is ABENABEMABY (treating Y here as a vowel).

You can make up your own secret language to use with your friends. The odder it sounds, the better. Why not try OSH- before vowels? You could drive people bananas with words like BOSHANOSHANOSHAS ! (Get it? BANANAS).

Mind-reading

Mind-reading acts used to be very popular on the stage. You could do one yourself at a party. All you need is an ''accomplice'' and a simple spoken code.

You place a pack of cards on a table and say that, while you are out of the room, you want someone to pick a card, show it to the others, and replace it in the pack. Your accomplice makes sure that he or she offers the pack to the others and replaces it on the table. This is important, because the position of the pack on the table will tell you which suit the card is. Placed slightly to the front of the table means Spades, to the back Diamonds, to the right Hearts, and to the left Clubs.

So when you return to the room, you know immediately the suit of the card. Say the card chosen is the Jack of Hearts. You ask the people to concentrate their minds on the card. You pretend to concentrate yourself,

Placed slightly to the right the pack of cards indicates a Heart

and then you say ''It's coming to me ... I think it's a red card. Is that right?'' This is where you get your next piece of assistance. Most of the people will murmur or call out something, but you will be taking note of how

your accomplice answers. There are four answers, which are codes for groups of cards:

"Yes" = 2, 3, 4, 5
"Right" = 6, 7, 8, 9
"Correct" = 10, J, Q, K
A nod = Ace

If the card was an Ace, a nod from your accomplice would be enough to identify it. But the answer for a Jack is "Correct".

After asking them to concentrate harder, you then use the other piece of information you know: "It's a Heart, isn't it?" Again you watch for your accomplice's answer. This time it's "Right", because the Jack is the second card in the group of 10,J,Q,K.

After more concentration and thought you blurt out "It's the Jack of Hearts!" - amazement and congratulations from your audience!

A word of warning - this "mind-reading" trick needs practice to make sure you get it right.

Hidden answers

After all that brainwork used up working out codes, here's something that won't tax your mind so much. See if you can find the hidden words or names in the following sentences.

Hidden countries
1 Co-operation between Interpol and national police forces is essential.
2 The new zoo buys one new pelican a day.
3 The tramway itself ran centrally through the main street.
4 The following September, mud appeared where lakes had previously been.
5 After the great wind, I am sure there will be rain.

Hidden animals
1 To obtain the finest fruit, I germinate the seeds myself.
2 The hospital is for those either mentally ailing, or ill and in general bad health.
3 We, as elected members of the Council, must take full responsibility.
4 As naked flames are forbidden in the mines, I suggest you take a torch.
5 The price minimum on keyboard instruments depends on age and quality.

Hidden cities
1 Geese on the seat, hens on the table - what a farmhouse!
2 Fred will be with me when we meet - OK? Your loving mother.

3 Hans van Larsen, the Dutch lawyer, was interested in burghers' rights.
4 If you travel in Korea, a Wonsan franc is collected at the airport.
5 It will not help that swelling to neglect the proper treatment.

Hidden birds
1 Can a rye grass succeed in a climate like this?
2 Home of a typical nocturnal bat, Ross Island lies just off the shore.
3 Mother was not amused, despite a gleam in her eye.
4 As the cage door was open, guinea-pigs were all over the room.
5 The answer's not a sparrow! Look a bit closer.

Hidden rivers
1 Soon I leave this country for a boat tour of the world.
2 After the first thud, sonic boom waves were blamed for the damage.
3 Of course I need further supplies to be delivered regularly.
4 When meat is used with spaghetti, gristle, fat and bone must be removed.
5 Whether the city is hindu or Muslim, pop over to the local bazaars.

8 TRICKS OF THE MIND

Have you got a good memory? Can you remember what you did every night last week? Perhaps you go to a club regularly on Monday nights, and watch a particular TV programme on Tuesdays, and maybe last Wednesday you were preparing for a French test on Thursday morning, and Thursday is the night when your best friend comes over. These things are all memory joggers, and you could probably go through the whole week and fill in what you were doing every night. But what about three months ago, or last year? That's not so easy. Well, perhaps it does not matter. But if you find it difficult to remember important things, there are many little tricks to help you. These are called "mnemonics" (you don't pronounce the first "m").

The tray test

There are 10 items set out on the tray below. Study them for 30 seconds and then turn the book over and try to remember them. Write them down on a piece of paper.

How did you fare? Were there one or two that you missed? There's a simple method for remembering lists of things, but it takes a litle practice. The idea is to have pictures in your mind which you connect each item to. Let's try to remember 10 items in order.

First we must think of 10 visual memories, one for each number. You can conjure up any 10 pictures you like, so long as you then don't have any trouble connecting them to the right number! A good method is to rhyme the numbers. For example, "one" and "run" - think of a runner, your favourite runner, their arms in the air as they win a race ... but in one hand is the first item. This might sound silly, but the sillier and more visual the "peg", the easier it is to remember the item.

Carrying on from there, "two, stew" - a stew pot, with the chef bringing something out on a ladle ... what is it? ... your second item. Three/tree (lots of your third item hanging like apples from branches), four/door (item sticking out of the letter box), five/hive (item covered with swarming bees and honey), six/kicks (player takes a penalty at soccer and as the ball flies into the net it turns into your item), seven/heaven (angel playing harp with your item), eight/skate (skater lifting his partner, no it's your eighth item), nine/wine (red wine spilt on a white tablecloth running over the ninth item), and ten/hen (laying tenth item).

Now you've got your 10 visual pegs. Write them down on a piece of paper next to the numbers and remember them. Don't read on until you have them firmly fixed in your mind. Now try remembering the 10 items on the tray at the bottom of the opposite page. Use your memory pegs.

Simple mnemonics

As we have just seen, rhymes make excellent memory-joggers. To remember certain spellings in English, there is the rhyme " 'i' before 'e' except after 'c' ". This helps us to remember words such as "believe", "siege" and "receive". There are exceptions, such as "weird", but then there are usually exceptions to every rule, and they have to be remembered individually.

Another good mnemonic is the initial letter. Take the colours of the rainbow - ROYGBIV, an easy word to say and remember. It stands, of course, for Red-Orange-Yellow-Green-Blue-Indigo-Violet.

You can make up your own mnemonics with initial letters. Say you are going shopping and need eggs, butter, milk and potatoes. The initial letters are E, B, M and P. Switch them around and you've got BEMP - not a real word, but easy enough to remember if you say it a few times. Sometimes you might be lucky and make a real word from you memory list. Or you might have no vowels and have to add one or two in, remembering, of course, that they don't belong. Try making up a word mnemonic for the following lists:

1 Ice-cream, Comic, Eggs, Milk.
2 Key-ring, Rice, Cornflakes, Bread

Linking

Another way to remember things is by linking them in your mind. Again, the more ridiculous the picture becomes, the easier it is to remember the links. Take these five items: Bus, newspaper, tennis racket, chocolate bar, kitten. Picture a *bus* in your mind - this is important as it is the key word of your list, whether it's just five items or 20 or more. Now think of the bus moving along the street and it knocks over a man reading a *newspaper*. You go to help and you see a picture in the newspaper of someone playing tennis with a huge *tennis racket*. But it's not hitting a ball, it's a *chocolate bar*, which lands next to a *kitten*, which picks it up and eats it. The kitten ... and so on, if you want to carry on with more items.

Right-tight

Do you have difficulty remembering which way to turn a screw or a water tap? Try this: right-tight, Left-Loose. Try making up your own mnemonics for remembering things you usually forget. What about directions - North, South, East and West? Starting with North at the top and going round in a clockwise direction, can you make up a mnemonic to help you remember the directions?

The second tray test

How did you get on with the items in the second tray test? Did you find that your memory pegs helped you to remember more items or to remember them more easily?

If you want to increase your visual memory "bank" to 20, here are some more rhymes, or in some cases near-rhymes.

Eleven - leavening (a cake, perhaps, with the item sticking up out of it). Twelve - shelve (you place the item on a shelf). From here you can make up your own pictures: thirteen/hurting, fourteen/courting, fifteen/lifting, sixteen/sick(ening), seventeen/eventing, eighteen/waiting, nineteen/pining, twenty/sentry.

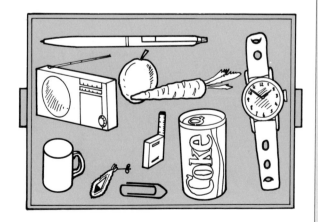

9 MORE TRICKS AND PROBLEMS

Missing symbol

See if you can find the missing symbol in the following series of symbols:

Now see if you can find the missing symbol in the sequence shown below:

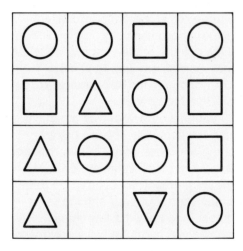

Bookworm

Three books of a three-volume set are standing on a shelf as shown in the picture. A bookworm tunnels its way through from page one of the first volume to the last page of volume three. The cardboard of the covers of each book is 2 mm thick, and the pages of each book occupy a total thickness of 302 mm. How far does the bookworm travel?

Crossing the river

There are many old problems about crossing a river in a rowing boat in which only one or two things can be ferried at a time. Here's the one about a wolf, a goat and a cabbage. A farmer has to get these across a river. But the wolf will eat the goat if left alone with it, and likewise the goat will eat the cabbage. It must have been a very small boat and a very large cabbage, because the farmer can take only one at a time across.

What is the fewest number of crossings the farmer has to make to get his three odd possessions across safely?

The orchard

A man has a house surrounded by an orchard. In his will he leaves the house to his wife and the orchard with its ten fruit trees to his five children. He states that each son and daughter must get two fruit trees and the same-shaped and same-sized piece of land. To comply with his will, how can the land be divided?

Plane crash

A Peruvian plane crashed in the jungle right on the border between Brazil and Bolivia. Where did they bury the survivors?

Arranging the cards

Separate all the aces and picture cards from a pack of playing cards. You should have 16 cards. Arrange them in four rows of four so that neither across nor down are there two cards of the same value or suit in the same row. In other words, each row across or downwards must have an ace, king, queen and jack as well as a spade, club, heart and diamond.

How the years fly!

A student is travelling on a plane during a vacation from university. A woman sitting next to her asks how old she is. "Well," says the student, who is studying Logic, "the day before yesterday I was only 19, but next year I shall be 22!"

What vacation was it - Easter, Summer or Christmas?

A tight squeeze

A lorry is stuck tight under a low bridge. The breakdown and fire services arrive, but no amount of pushing and pulling can free the lorry. Traffic is held up and a crowd gathers. A little boy watching the operation goes up to the policeman in control and tugs at his sleeve. At first the policeman ignores him, but then the boy whispers something in his ear. The policeman smiles, and in no time at all he manages to get the lorry free.

What did the little boy say?

It's a record

A gramophone record measures 30 cm across. There is an outer margin of 1 cm before the recording starts. The centre of the record, where the label is, measures 10 cm across. If there is an average of 40 grooves to the centimetre, how far does the needle travel when the record is played all the way through?

A balancing trick

Take an ordinary pencil and a penknife. Make the pencil as sharp as you can without breaking the point. Now try to balance the pencil with its point on the tip of your finger, keeping the finger perfectly still.

Turning the cards

Imagine four cards on a table. You are told that each card is either blank or shaded on one side, and has a picture of a cat or a dog on the other side. If they appear as shown below, which ones would you have to pick up and turn over to be able to answer the following question: Does every blank card have a dog on its other side?

Ball and jar

Here's a good party trick. You need a jar with a neck, and a ball smaller than the neck of the jar. A coffee jar and a tennis ball might do.

Stand the jar upside-down on the table over the ball. Now ask if anyone can carry the jar and ball round the room and return them to the table without touching the ball or turning the jar over. They may use only their hands. Before turning to the solution, see if you can do this yourself.

Clever measure

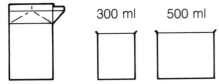

300 ml   500 ml

A recipe calls for 400 ml of milk. You have a carton of milk and two containers, one holding 300 ml the other 500 ml. How do you measure out the 400 ml you need?

The messenger

A motorcycle messenger arrived at an office with an important package. At the reception desk, he asked for Mrs Peters. "I have to hand this package over to Mrs Peters personally and get her to sign for it," he explained. "Well," said the receptionist, "as a matter of fact, I am Mrs Peters."

The messenger was about to hand over the packet, but hesitated. "Er ... I'm sorry," he said, "How do I know you *are* Mrs Peters?" The receptionist smiled. "I think I can prove that," she said, reaching for her handbag. She produced a photograph of herself and showed the messenger. "There, do you recognize me?" she asked. "Oh, yes," said the messenger, quite satisfied. "Here's your parcel. Just sign here, please."

Was he right to hand over the package?

The ship's ladder

A ship lay at anchor in a harbour with a rope ladder hanging from the deck down into the water. At 4.30 pm, six rungs at the bottom of the ladder were underwater. The rungs were 25 cm apart and the thickness of each rung was 2 cm. If the tide was rising at 40 cm an hour, how many rungs were underwater at 6.30 pm?

Mothers and daughters

Two mothers and two daughters go into a sweet shop and spend £2 each. Yet the shopkeeper takes in only £6. How come?

Cutting the ribbon

A schoolteacher has to cut a roll of ribbon into metre lengths. It takes her one second to measure and cut off one metre. If the ribbon is 60 metres in length, how long does it take the teacher to cut up all the lengths?

The frightened explorer

An explorer woke up early one morning and after having breakfast travelled south for 2 km. It was hard going, so he had to stop for a breather. As he prepared to get going again, he saw a bear in the distance, so he set off towards the east this time to avoid the creature, who looked rather hungry. After travelling in this direction for 2 km, he came to a sudden stop when he spied another bear prowling around. Then he saw some more. The only way to escape was to go due north, which he did, as fast as he could travel. After 2 km he arrived back at his overnight camp. OK so far? Right, now see if you can work out what colour the bears were.

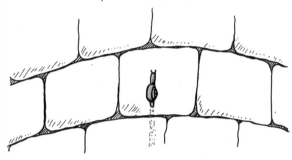

The climbing snail

A snail is at the bottom of a well 22 metres deep. It begins to crawl up very slowly, at snail's pace in fact! It takes a day for it to climb 7 metres, but every night it slides back 2 metres. How long does it take for the snail to reach the top of the well?

Lucky dip

There are three boxes. One contains two black draughts, another has two white draughts, and the third has one draught of each colour. The boxes have been labelled according to what they contain - BB for two black draughts, WW two white, and BW for one of each. Now someone mixes up the labels so that none of the boxes has the correct label.

Without looking inside the boxes, you are allowed to put in your hand and take out one draught at a time from any box. You may continue to do this until you can say what each box holds.

How many draughts would you need to withdraw, and from which box or boxes?

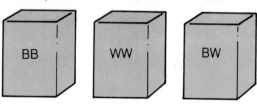

Not chess

We'll end with a difficult one. You need a chessboard and 32 dominoes that will each cover two squares on the board. Now if you cut off two diagonally opposite squares of the board (don't do this, just cover them up), and put one of the dominoes back in its box, can you cover the remaining 62 squares on the board with the 31 dominoes? If it can't be done you have to prove it.

You could spend a great deal of time shifting dominoes around the cut-down board. But if you stop to think about the problem, you might just come up with the solution without even looking at a board or any dominoes.

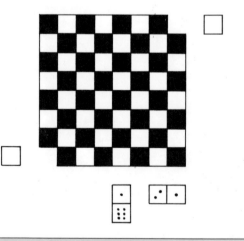

ANSWERS

1 LATERAL THINKING

Father and son
They were husband and wife. Most people first think that "two Americans" refers to two men. If this were the case, the problem would be impossible. You have to get away from your "logical" line of thought to solve it.

Bottles and knives
The three knives are interlaced as shown in the diagram.

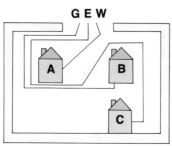

The dream
If the man in the doctor's story had really died in his sleep, no one else could possibly have known what his dream had been about.

Houses and pipes
The pipes can be laid in a number of ways. The illustration shows one way.

Cutting a postcard
This needs a sharp knife and a ruler, so don't try it yourself unless supervised by an adult. Cut the card carefully as shown in the diagrams. First, fold the card down the centre as shown in 'A' and cut down the fold to within 5 mm of each end. It will look like diagram A. Next, with the card folded, make more cuts all along the card about 3 mm apart, as shown in diagram B. The cuts

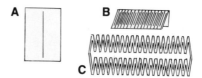

should be made alternately from the fold of the card and from the edge, each cut stopping within 5 mm of the opposite side. When you have made all of the cuts, open out the card, and it will look like diagram C. If you open it out still further, very carefully, you will be able to form a large loop, big enough for an average person to pass through.

Multiplying amoebas
It takes 4 hours and 5 minutes. After 5 minutes, the amoeba in the first jar will have split into two, and we know it takes two amoebas 4 hours to fill the jar.

The portrait
It's a portrait of the owner's son.

The next letter
The next letter in the series is E. The letters are the initial letters of numbers - One, Two, Three, and so on!

Unspillable water
Fill a glass with water right up to the brim. Rest a piece of flat, strong card over the top of the glass. Now place one hand on top of the card and, holding it in place, turn the glass over with your other hand. You can now remove your hand from the card and it will stay in place. The water should not run out. Now place the upturned glass on a flat surface - an upturned plate on the draining-board of the sink would be safest. Carefully slide the card away. The water will still stay in the glass. But now no one will be able to lift the glass without spilling the water.

Only one match
The match!

Foxy Foxwell
Foxy was stealing wheelbarrows!

A handy trick
Their right elbow.

There's no law against it!
If the listener had a widow, he would be in no position to marry again. He'd be dead!

Family fun
Ten. There is one daughter, who is a sister to all seven sons, so 8 children and 2 adults make 10.

Hard-boiled eggs
A person cannot eat more than one egg on an empty stomach. After that, the person's stomach is no longer empty!

2 MANIPULATING MATCHES

Halving the squares
The dotted lines indicate the matches removed.

Squarebashing
Don't forget the larger square in (a) makes six squares altogether.

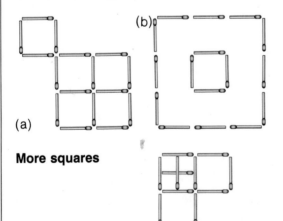

(a)

(b)

More squares

Pigpens
Here is farmer Crockfoot's new pigpen. Clever, isn't it?

Making nines
Using 11 matches:

Using 3 matches:

Touching matches

A Roman problem

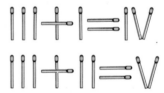

Triangulation
Make one triangle on the table and then stand the others up to make a pyramid, giving you three more triangles.

Making triangles

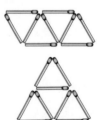

Match trick
The secret is to bend the match first. Now it will nearly always land on its edge. Try it and see.

3 ODD ONE OUT

Odd one out
1 SHARK, a fish (the others are MAMMALS)
2 PRETORIA, a city (others COUNTRIES)
3 SHAKESPEARE, a writer (others PAINTERS)
4 BAT, a mammal (others BIRDS)
5 SMOKE (others forms of WATER)
6 XYLOPHONE (others STRINGED INSTRUMENTS)
7 CUBE (others TWO-DIMENSIONAL FIGURES)
8 TORONTO, Canadian city (others in USA)
9 GREYHOUND, a dog (others in CAT family)
10 METRE, a measurement (others MONEY)
11 EVERGLADES, swamp (others MOUNTAIN RANGES)
12 EGGS from a chicken (others from a COW)
13 BADMINTON (others played with BALL) *or* SQUASH (others played over NET)
14 PLUTONIUM, metal (others GASES)
15 SUPERIOR, lake (others RIVERS)
16 BACKGAMMON, boardgame (others CARD GAMES)
17 SIRIUS, star (others PLANETS)
18 EAGLE (others FLIGHTLESS birds)
19 JACK OF SPADES (others have TWO EYES)
20 SPIDER, arachnid (others are INSECTS)

4 FUN WITH COINS

A "coin-fidence" trick
The coin was obviously a fake and the farmer was trying to pull a confidence trick on the auction house. No coins have BC on them. BC, which means "before Christ", was a term invented long after the birth of Christ for dating events in the past.

Touching coins

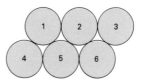

With the coins numbered as above, here are the three moves:
1 Slide 6 round to touch 4 and 5
2 Slide 5 under 2 and 3
3 Slide 3 to touch 5 and 6
The final position will form a circle as here:

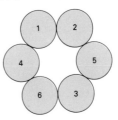

Space for No. 5
Start with the coins as in diagram A. Move coin 1 round to touch coins 4 and 2 as in diagram B. Then carefully slide coin 4 down and round so that it touches coins 3 and 2, as in diagram C. You can now slide the fifth coin into the space just vacated by coin 4. Easy when you know how!

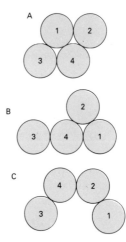

Changing places
Make the following moves: 3→4 5→3 6→5 4→6 2→4 1→2 3→1 5→3 7→5 6→7 4→6 2→4 3→2 5→3 4→5

Up-ending the pyramid

Move coin 1 to make a row by itself below 8

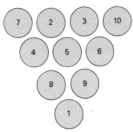

and 9. Then move 7 to the left of 2, and 10 to the right of 3. You will finish up with the pyramid reversed.

A simple sum

20p and 5p. Only one of the coins is not a 20p piece.

5 A WAY WITH WORDS

Word records

Five-letter words that have four vowels include EErIE and qUEUE. The word with five vowels in a row is qUEUEIng. The eight-letter word with only one vowel is strEngth. The word connected with magic that has five consonants in a row is wiTCHCRaft. (Another one with five consecutive consonants is streNGTHS). The word with three consecutive pairs of letters is bOOKKEEping. The "before and after" words are ORatOR and UNDergroUND.

Sounds the same

1 (a) fir, (b) fur; **2** (a) colonel, (b) kernel; **3** (a) seller, (b) cellar; **4** (a) leak, (b) leek; **5** (a) lynx, (b) links; **6** (a) ruff, (b) rough; **7** (a) lier, (b) lyre; **8** (a) aisle, (b) isle; **9** (a) tee, (b) tea; **10** (a) bold, (b) bowled; **11** (a) berry, (b) bury; **12** (a) nun, (b) none; **13** (a) minor, (b) miner; **14** (a) gorilla, (b) guerrilla; **15** (a) ton, (b) tun; **16** (a) sew, (b) sow; **17** (a) cent, (b) scent; **18** (a) beach, (b) beech; **19** (a) stair, (b) stare; **20** (a) toad, (b) towed.

Double words

1 clog, **2** grave, **3** painter, **4** bill, **5** top, **6** loaf, **7** peer, **8** flat, **9** hop, **10** trifle, **11** firm, **12** type, **13** ring, **14** date, **15** shed, **16** lean, **17** coach, **18** mean, **19** vessel, **20** club.

Back-and-forth words

1 EWE. **2** DEED. **3** PEEP. **4** NOON. **5** LEVEL. **6** KAYAK. **7** MINIM. **8** DEIFIED.

Palindromes can also be phrases or sentences. Among the best known are "Madam, I'm Adam" (how Adam introduced himself to Eve in the Garden of Eden) and "Able was I ere I saw Elba", which is what Napoleon might have said when he was banished to the island of Elba (except that he spoke French!).

See if you can make up a phrase or sentence that reads backwards, letter by letter, the same as it reads forwards.

Anagrams

1 ROSE, **2** ELEPHANTS, **3** THOUSAND, **4** TABLE-TENNIS, **5** WASHINGTON, **6** SUBMARINE, **7** NEIL ARMSTRONG, **8** WILLIAM SHAKESPEARE, **9** ADAM AND EVE, **10** RATTLESNAKE, **11** ASTRONOMERS, **12** PUNISHMENT, **13** THE EYES, **14** SCHOOLMASTER, **15** SEPARATION, **16** TWO PLUS ELEVEN.

The answer to the last anagram is there for all to see - ONE WORD !

Spot the error

1   "There are . . ."
2   "sentence"
3   The third mistake is that there are only two!

Doublets

The following solutions are not necessarily the only ways to complete the doublets. You might have found other ways, or even quicker ways!. **1** CAT-COT-DOT-DOG, **2** POOR-BOOR-BOOK-ROOK-ROCK-RICK-RICH, **3** LIVE-LINE-LANE-LAND-LEND-LEAD-DEAD, **4** DUST-GUST-GIST-GILT-GILD-GOLD, **5** BLACK-SLACK-STACK-STALK-STALE-SHALE-WHALE-WHILE-WHITE.

Word-finding
1 Brown-green-yellow-blue-mauve

2 India-Iceland-Germany-Mexico

3 Ape-cheetah-lion-weasel-zebra

6 PARADOXES

Bottle and cork
The cork costs ½p (and the bottle (10½p).

Packing them in
This sounds at first as if the hotel manager had done the impossible. But if you think about it, when he went back to get the sixth couple, they were actually the second couple. I'm afraid the sixth couple had to sleep in the linen cupboard!

A basket of eggs
She started with 31 eggs in her basket. Half of 31 eggs plus half an egg is $15\frac{1}{2} + \frac{1}{2}$, that is 16 eggs, leaving 15 eggs. Work it through and you will find that she was left with one egg. Why is it important the eggs were free range? Well, that's for the hens' sake. How would you like to be a battery hen?

Dividing up the gold
The man with 5 bottles should get 7 gold coins, the man with 3 bottles only 1 coin. This might sound unfair, but look at it this way. Let's say they got 3 glasses of water from each bottle, or 24 glasses in all. They shared the water equally, so each drank 8 glasses of water. The man with 5 bottles supplied 15 glasses of water. He drank 8 of these himself, so he contributed 7 glasses to the old man. The other friend supplied 3 bottles, or 9 glasses of water - 8 for himself and just 1 for the old man.

Having worked this out, the two friends decided to give all the gold to their village council for digging a new well. After all, it's the thought that counts.

The missing pound
You can drive yourself mad thinking about this one. What actually happened was that the £27 the diners paid for their meal *included* the £2 that the waiter kept. The cost of the meal was £25 and the waiter took £2. Perhaps he thought he deserved a tip!

Passing trains
When they *meet*, both trains are the same distance from Omsk however fast they were travelling.

Sharing the elephants
The sons could not possibly comply with their father's will because the fractions one-half, one-third and one-ninth do not total one. Try adding them up and you will get seventeen-eighteenths. However, the solution proposed was the only one that would satisfy the RSPCA!

7 CODES AND SECRETS

Simple ciphers
THE ENEMY SOLDIERS ARE TWO DAYS' MARCH AWAY

Changing the code
VIMRJSVGIQIRXW RIIHIH; STRIKE AT DAWN

Using a codeword
ATTACK becomes QNBCMA. FOUREBE is deciphered as VICTORY.

Secret symbols
PIGPEN SYMBOLS

Spoken codes
DO YOU LIKE HIM? I DO.

Hidden answers
Hidden countries: **1** Poland, **2** Canada,
3 France, **4** Bermuda, **5** India
Hidden animals: **1** tiger, **2** gorilla, **3** weasel,
4 snake, **5** monkey
Hidden cities: **1** Athens, **2** Tokyo,
3 Edinburgh, **4** San Francisco, **5** Wellington
Hidden birds: **1** canary, **2** albatross, **3** eagle,
4 penguin, **5** owl
Hidden rivers: **1** Nile, **2** Hudson,
3 Seine, **4** Tigris, **5** Limpopo

8 TRICKS OF THE MIND

Simple mnemonics
1 MICE, 2 BRICK (add the 'I').

Right-tight
Try this rhyme:

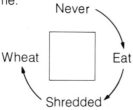

9 MORE TRICKS AND PROBLEMS

Missing symbol

The symbols represent the numbers 1,2,3 etc
coupled with their mirror images. Just take a
straight piece of paper and cover up the left
side of the symbols.

Starting at the top and reading each row from
left to right, you will discover the sequence.
The first symbol, followed by the first and
second symbol, then the first, second and
third symbol, and so on.

Bookworm
The bookworm travels 310 mm. Look
carefully at the books as they stand on the
shelf. Page one of the first volume is on the
right of that volume, so the bookworm travels
only through the front cover of volume 1. It
then travels completely through volume 2,
but only through the back cover of volume 3
before it reaches the last page of that volume
(on the left of the book as it is placed on the
shelf). The distances add up as follows:

Front cover, volume 1	2 mm
Back cover, volume 2	2 mm
Pages, volume 2	302 mm
Front cover, volume 2	2 mm
Back cover, volume 3	2 mm
Total	310 mm

Crossing the river
Seven crossings. First, the farmer takes the
goat across, leaving the wolf with the
cabbage. He returns without a passenger and
then takes either wolf or cabbage (let's say
the wolf) across. He leaves the wolf on the
other side and brings the goat back. Then he
takes the cabbage across and leaves it with
the wolf. He returns for the goat and brings it
across.

The orchard
The land was divided as shown here:

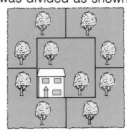

Plane crash
You don't bury survivors!

Arranging the cards
There are many ways in which the cards may
be laid out. The diagram shows one. A quick
way to solve this puzzle is to start by laying
out the aces, say, in a diagonal starting from
the top left-hand corner. Next, lay out the
kings in the diagonal from the top right-hand

corner, making sure you do not get an ace and a king of the same suit in any row. It is then fairly easy to place the queens next to the top-right and bottom-left corners, and the jacks in the remaining spaces, making sure again to keep the suits different.

How the years fly!
It was the Christmas vacation, because it had to be on January 1st. On 30 December, the student was still 19. Her birthday had to be 31 December, when she was 20. She would be 21 on 31 December next (the same year), so she would be 22 the following year.

A tight squeeze
The little boy suggested that they let some air out of the lorry's tyres! As soon as this was done, the top of the lorry came away from the bridge and the driver was able to reverse it out and try another route.

It's a record
About 9 cm. The needle doesn't travel round the record, so the number of grooves per centimetre has nothing to do with the problem. The needle travels in a direction across the grooves towards the centre of the record. Its path is not quite in a straight line, being slightly curved, so it travels a bit more than 9 cm.

A balancing trick
The trick here is that you need the penknife to help balance the pencil! Open the penknife and stick the blade into the pencil about a third of the way up from the point, as shown

in the picture. The penknife has to be only partly opened, and you will need to experiment to get it right.

Turning the cards
You would need to turn over cards 1 and 3 - not card 4 as many people think. You need to turn over card 1, because if it has a cat on the other side the answer to the question is "no". You need to turn over card 3, because if it is blank the answer is again "no". Card 2 does not matter, because we are concerned only with blank cards. Finally, whatever card 4 has on the other side, the answer to the question cannot be "no". Try the two alternatives yourself.

Ball and jar
There is a simple trick to this which you can do with just a little practice. Hold the jar in both hands. As you slide it off the table, you make circular movements so that the ball starts moving round the neck of the jar. You will find that it stays in the jar so long as you keep it moving. It's a bit like a hula hoop, if you've ever tried keeping one going round your body.

Clever measure
First you fill the 500 ml container from the carton (1), and then you fill the 300 ml container from the 500 ml container, which will now have 200 ml left (2). Empty the 300 ml container back into the carton (3). Now pour the 200 ml from the larger container into

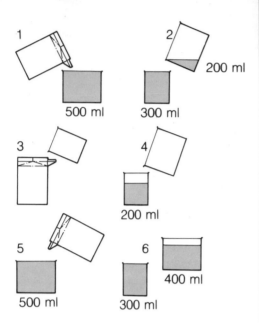

the smaller one (4). Fill the larger container again from the carton (5). Now if you fill the smaller container from the larger one, it will take another 100 ml. This will leave the larger container with 400 ml, just the amount of milk you need (6).

The messenger
Of course not. The receptionist proved nothing except that the photograph was of herself.

The ship's ladder
Six. As the ship is afloat, the water level in relation to the ship stays the same, so the same number of rungs are underwater.

Mothers and daughters
There are only three women - a girl with her mother and grandmother.

Cutting the ribbon
59 seconds. The last cut separates the last two lengths, so a 60th cut is not necessary.

The frightened explorer
The bears were white. If he travelled south for 2 km, east for 2 km and then north for 2 km and arrived back at the same place, he must have been at the North Pole! You can see this easily if you draw his path on an

orange. (There are places near the South Pole where you could make a similar trip, but there are no bears in Antarctica.)

Lucky dip
Just one - from the box labelled BW. If it is a black draught, you know that box must contain two black draughts, because it is wrongly labelled. Now, if you turn to the box labelled WW, it cannot be the true WW and you've already discovered the true BB. So WW must be the true BW. That leaves BB, which must be the true WW. You would be able to work out their contents in exactly the same way if you had drawn a white draught from the first box.

The climbing snail
It takes 4 days. The snail climbs 5 metres over a period of 24 hours, so at the end of the third night it has covered 15 metres. It climbs another 7 metres by the end of the fourth day, so is at the top before it starts slipping back again during the night.

Not chess
The secret here, if you think about it, is that each domino has to cover one black and one white square, because only squares of different colours are next to each other. Diagonally opposite corners are the same colour, so if you remove them from the board you leave it with 32 squares of one colour and only 30 of the other. So after covering 30 black and 30 white squares with dominoes, you are left with two squares of the same colour. They cannot be next to each other, so you can't cover them with your remaining domino.